101 SHOWTUNES FC

PIANO/ORGAN ED

G000292344

Wise Publications
London/New York/Paris/Sydney/Copenhagen/Madrid

Exclusive Distributors:
Music Sales Limited
8/9 Frith Street, London W1V 5TZ, England.
Music Sales Pty Limited
120 Rothschild Avenue, Rosebery, NSW 2018, Australia.

Order No. AM32509
ISBN 0-7119-0236-4
This book © Copyright 1983, 1995 by Wise Publications

Printed in the United Kingdom by
Scotprint Limited, Musselburgh, Edinburgh.

Your Guarantee of Quality
As publishers, we strive to produce every book to
the highest commercial standards.
This book has been carefully designed to minimise awkward page
turns and to make playing from it a real pleasure.
Particular care has been given to specifying acid-free, neutral-sized paper
made from pulps which have not been elemental chlorine bleached.
This pulp is from farmed sustainable forests and was produced with
special regard for the environment.
Throughout, the printing and binding have been planned to ensure a sturdy,
attractive publication which should give years of enjoyment.
If your copy fails to meet our high standards, please inform us
and we will gladly replace it.

Music Sales' complete catalogue describes thousands of titles and is available in
full colour sections by subject, direct from Music Sales Limited.
Please state your areas of interest and send a cheque/postal order for £1.50 for postage to:
Music Sales Limited, Newmarket Road, Bury St. Edmunds, Suffolk IP33 3YB.

1
Big Spender

Words by Dorothy Fields
Music by Cy Coleman

2
The Candy Man

Words & Music by Leslie Bricusse & Anthony Newley

3
Good Morning Starshine

Words by James Rado & Gerome Ragni
Music by Galt MacDermot

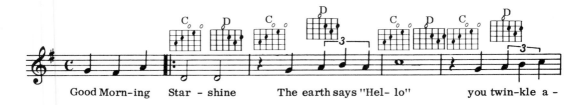

Good Morn-ing Star - shine The earth says "Hel- lo" you twin-kle a -

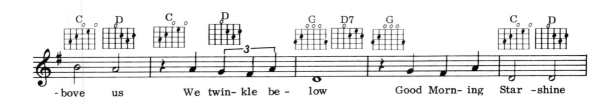

- bove us We twin- kle be - low Good Morn- ing Star -shine

you lead us a - long My love and me as we sing____ our

ear - ly morn-ing sing - ing song. Glid - dy glup gloo- py Nib - by nab-by noo-py La

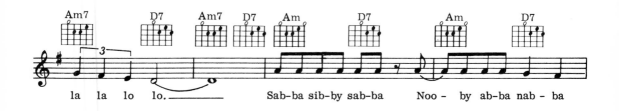

la la lo lo.____ Sab-ba sib-by sab-ba Noo - by ab-ba nab - ba

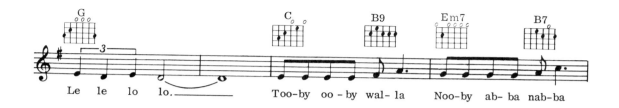

Le le lo lo._____ Too-by oo-by wal-la Noo-by ab-ba nab-ba

Ear-ly morn-ing sing-ing song___ Good Morn-ing Sing-ing a song

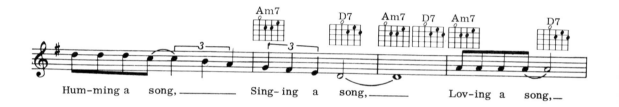

Hum-ming a song,_____ Sing-ing a song,_____ Lov-ing a song,__

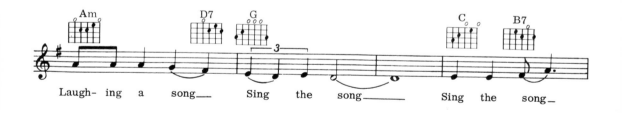

Laugh-ing a song___ Sing the song_____ Sing the song_

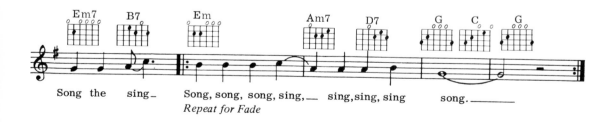

Song the sing_ Song, song, song, sing,___ sing,sing, sing song._____

Repeat for Fade

4
I Can't Give You Anything But Love

Words by Dorothy Fields
Music by Jimmy McHugh

Andante con moto

Gee, but it's tough to be broke, kid, — It's not a joke, kid, It's a curse;
Rome was-n't built in a day, kid, — You have to pay, kid, For what you get,

Think that you ought to be know-ing, — My luck is go-ing — from bad to worse.
But I am will-ing to wait, dear, — Your lit-tle mate, dear, — will not for-get.

Who knows some day I will win too, I'll be-gin to reach my prime.
You have a life-time be-fore you, I'll a-dore you, come what may.

Now, tho' I see what our end is, — All I can spend is just my time.
Please don't be blue for the pre-sent, — When it's so plea-sant to hear you say,

Chorus

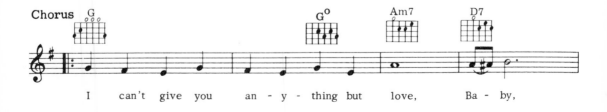

I can't give you an-y-thing but love, Ba-by,

5
Who Can I Turn To
Words & Music by Leslie Bricusse & Anthony Newley

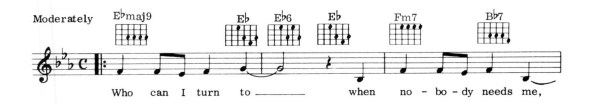

Who can I turn to _____ when no - bo - dy needs me,

_____ My heart wants to know, and so I must go where des - ti-ny leads me,

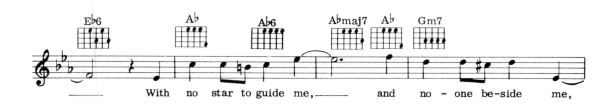

_____ With no star to guide me, _____ and no - one be-side me,

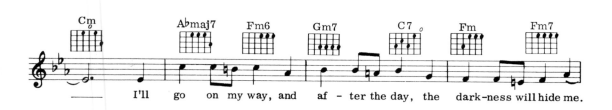

_____ I'll go on my way, and af - ter the day, the dark-ness will hide me.

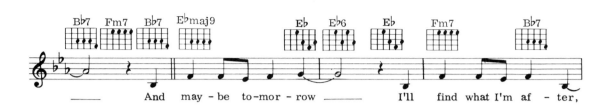

And may-be to-mor-row ____ I'll find what I'm af - ter,

____ I'll throw off my sor - row, beg, steal or bor-row my share of laugh-ter,

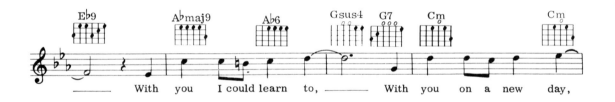

____ With you I could learn to, ____ With you on a new day,

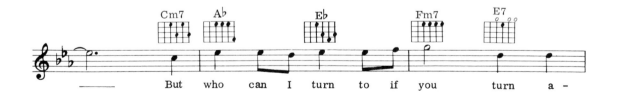

____ But who can I turn to if you turn a -

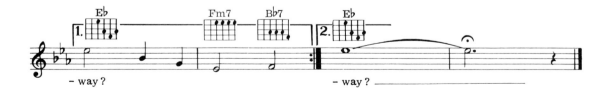

- way? ____ - way? ____

6
What Kind Of Fool Am I

Words & Music by Leslie Bricusse & Anthony Newley

Slowly, with expression

What kind of fool am I ——— who nev - er

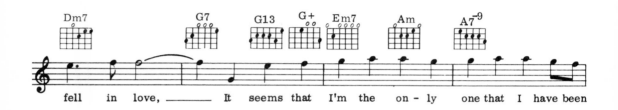

fell in love, ——— It seems that I'm the on - ly one that I have been

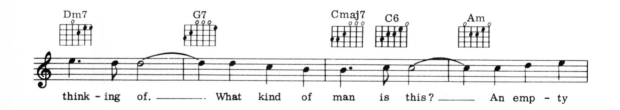

think - ing of. ——— What kind of man is this? ——— An emp - ty

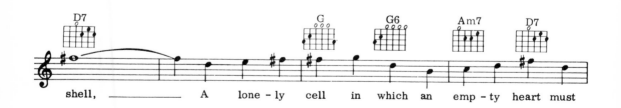

shell, ——— A lone - ly cell in which an emp - ty heart must

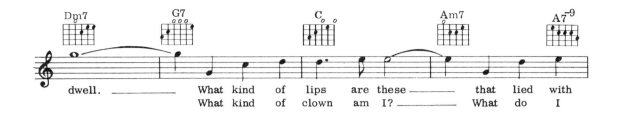

dwell. _____ What kind of lips are these _____ that lied with
What kind of clown am I? _____ What do I

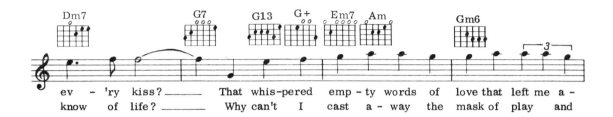

ev - 'ry kiss? _____ That whis-pered emp-ty words of love that left me a-
know of life? _____ Why can't I cast a - way the mask of play and

-lone like this. _____ Why can't I fall in love _____ like an - y
live my life? _____ Why can't I fall in love _____ till I don't

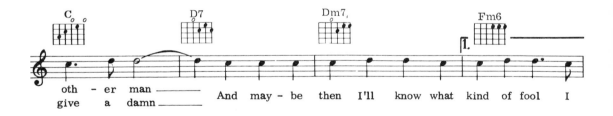

oth - er man _____ And may - be then I'll know what kind of fool I
give a damn _____

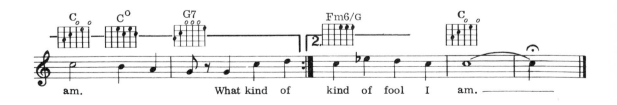

am.   What kind of kind of fool I am. _____

7
Burlington Bertie From Bow

Words & Music by William Hargreaves

I'm Bert, _____ p'raps you've heard of me; Bert, _____ you've had word of me; Jog-ging a - long, heart-y and strong, liv-ing on plates of fresh air. _____ I dress _____ up in fash-ion, and when I am feel-ing de - pressed, _____ I shave from my cuff all the whis-kers and fluff, stick my hat on and tod-dle up West. _____

Chorus

I'm Bur-ling-ton Ber-tie, I rise at ten thir-ty and saun-ter a - long like a toff. _____ I walk down the Strand with my gloves on my hand, then I walk down a - gain with them off. _____ I'm all airs and gra-ces, cor - rect ea - sy pa - ces, with - out food so

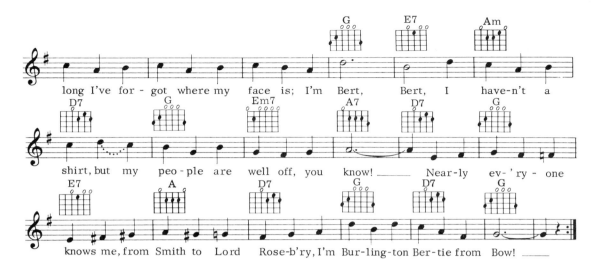

long I've for-got where my face is; I'm Bert, Bert, I have-n't a

shirt, but my peo-ple are well off, you know! ___ Near-ly ev-'ry-one

knows me, from Smith to Lord Rose-b'ry, I'm Bur-ling-ton Ber-tie from Bow! ___

2. I stroll with Lord Hurlington, roll in the Burlington,
   Call for champagne, walk out again, come back and borrow the ink.
   I live most expensive; like Tom Lipton, I'm in the swim.
   He's got so much 'oof' that he sleeps on the roof, and I live in the room over him.
   I'm Burlington Bertie, I rise at ten thirty then saunter along Temple Bar.
   As round there I skip I keep shouting, "Pip! Pip!", and the darn'd fools think I'm in my car.
   At Rothchild's I swank it, my body I plank it on his front doorstep with 'The Mail'
   for a blanket;
   I'm Bert, Bert, and Rothchild was hurt; he said, "You can't sleep there." I said, "Oh!"
   He said, "I'm Rothchild, sonny!" I said, "That's damn'd funny,
   I'm Burlington Bertie from Bow!"

3. I smile condescendingly while they're extending me
   Cheer upon cheer when I appear captain with my polo team.
   So strict are my people, they're William the Conqueror's strain.
   If they ever knew I'd been talking to you, why, they'd never look at me again!
   I'm Burlington Bertie, I rise at ten thirty and reach Kempton Park about three.
   I stand by the rail when a horse is for sale, and you ought to see Wooton watch me!
   I lean on some awning while Lord Derby's yawning, then he bids, "Two thousand,"
   and I bid, "Good morning;"
   I'm Bert, Bert, I'd buy one, a cert, but where could I keep it, you know!
   I can't let my man see me in bed with a gee-gee!
   I'm Burlington Bertie from Bow!

4. My pose, though ironical, shows that my monocle
   Holds up my face, keeps it in place, stops it from slipping away.
   Cigars, I smoke thousands; I usually deal in the Strand,
   But you've got to take care, when you're getting them there, or some idiot might stand
   on your hand.
   I'm Burlington Bertie, I rise at ten thirty then Buckingham Palace I view.
   I stand in the Yard while they're changing the guard, and the King shouts across, "Toodle-oo!"
   The Prince of Wales' brother, along with some other, slaps me on the back and says,
   "Come and see mother."
   I'm Bert, Bert, and royalty's hurt when they ask me to dine I say, "No.
   I've just had a banana with Lady Diana;
   I'm Burlington Bertie from Bow!"

8
I Wanna Be Around

Words & Music by Johnny Mercer & Sadie Vimmerstedt

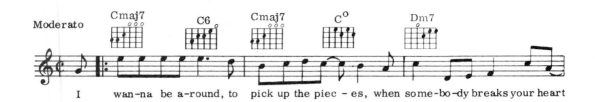

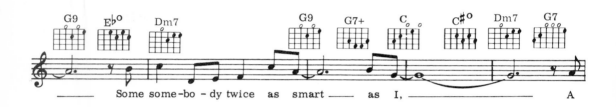

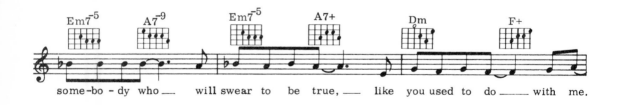

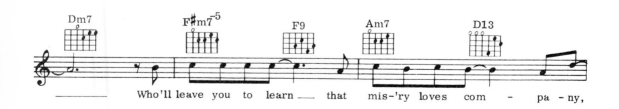

wait and see!_____ I wan-na be a-round, to see how he does__it when
she

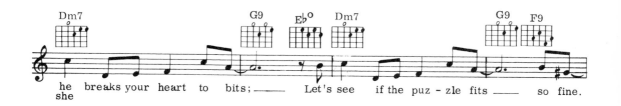

he breaks your heart to bits; _____ Let's see if the puz-zle fits ____ so fine.
she

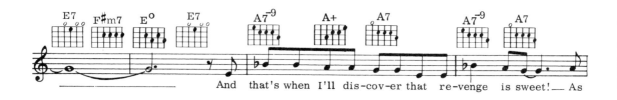

_____ And that's when I'll dis-cov-er that re-venge is sweet!__ As

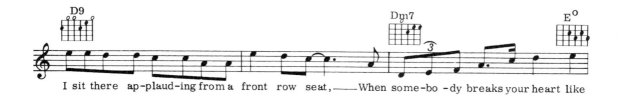

I sit there ap-plaud-ing from a front row seat, _____ When some-bo-dy breaks your heart like

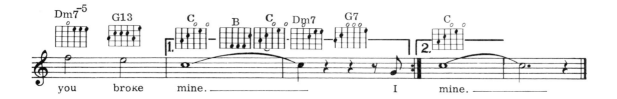

you broke mine. _____ I mine. _____

9
A Wonderful Day Like Today

Words & Music by Leslie Bricusse & Anthony Newley

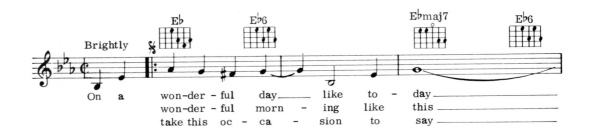

On a won-der-ful day___ like to-day___
won-der-ful morn-ing like this___
take this oc-ca-sion to say___

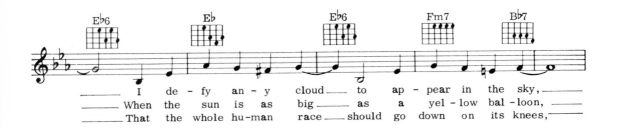

___ I de-fy an-y cloud___ to ap-pear in the sky,___
___ When the sun is as big___ as a yel-low bal-loon,___
___ That the whole hu-man race___ should go down on its knees,___

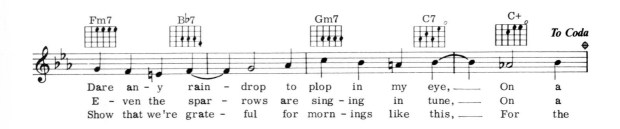

To Coda

Dare an-y rain-drop to plop in my eye,___ On a
E - ven the spar-rows are sing-ing in tune,___ On a
Show that we're grate-ful for morn-ings like this,___ For the

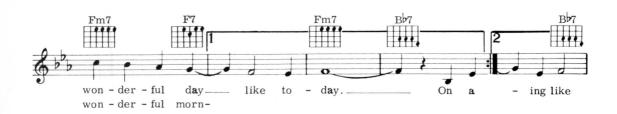

won-der-ful day___ like to-day.___ On a ___-ing like
won-der-ful morn-

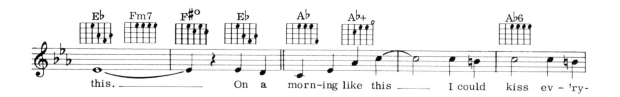

this. _____ On a morn-ing like this _____ I could kiss ev-'ry-

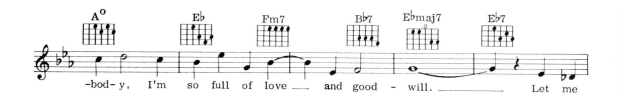

-bod-y, I'm so full of love _____ and good - will. _____ Let me

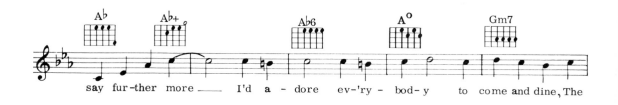

say fur-ther more _____ I'd a - dore ev-'ry - bod-y to come and dine, The

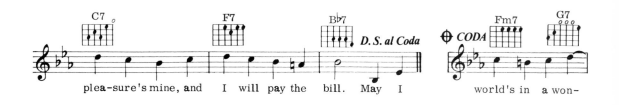

D. S. al Coda *CODA*

plea-sure's mine, and I will pay the bill. May I world's in a won-

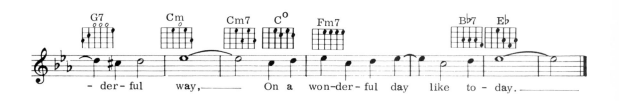

- der-ful way, _____ On a won-der-ful day like to - day. _____

10
Diamonds Are A Girl's
Best Friend

Words by Leo Robin
Music by Jule Styne

March tempo   F

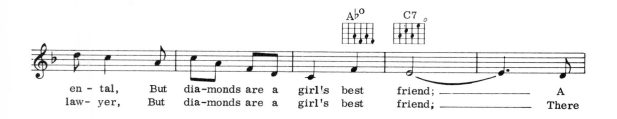

1. A   kiss   on   the   hand   may   be   quite   con - tin -
2. (There) may   come   a   time   when   a   lass   needs   a

en - tal,   But   dia-monds are   a   girl's   best   friend; ——————   A
law- yer,   But   dia-monds are   a   girl's   best   friend; ——————   There

kiss   may   be   grand   but   it   won't   pay   the   rent - al   on   your
may   come   a   time   when   a   hard   boiled   em - ploy - er   thinks you're

hum - ble   flat, ——   Or   help   you   at   the   Au - to - mat.
aw - ful   nice ——   But   get   that   "ice"   or   else   no   dice.

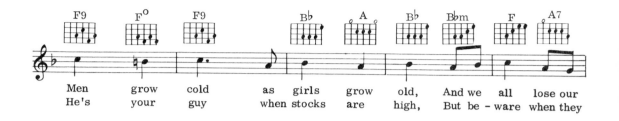

Men grow cold as girls grow old, And we all lose our
He's your guy when stocks are high, But be - ware when they

charms in the end; _____ But square cut or pear shape, these
start to de - scend; _____ It's then that those lous - es go

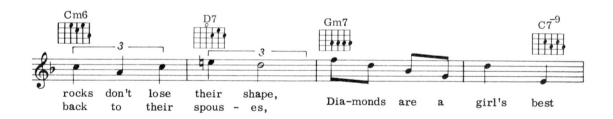

rocks don't lose their shape, Dia-monds are a girl's best
back to their spous - es,

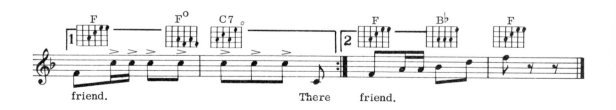

friend. There friend.

11
Pennies From Heaven

Words by John Burke
Music by Arthur Johnston

12
Can't Help Falling In Love

Words & Music by George Weiss, Hugo Peretti & Luigi Creatore

Wise men say _____ on - ly fools rush
Shall I stay, _____ would it be a

in, But I can't help fall - ing in
sin, If I can't help fall - ing in

love with you. Like a riv - er flows
love with you.

sure - ly to the sea, Dar - ling so it goes, some things ___ are meant to

be. Take my hand _____ take my

whole life too, For I can't

help fall - ing in love with you.

opt. D.S. al Fine

13
Gonna Build A Mountain

Words & Music by Leslie Bricusse & Anthony Newley

Quickstep tempo

1. Gon - na build a moun-tain, from a lit - tle
2. Gon - na build a day - dream, from a lit - tle

hill, Gon-na build a moun-tain, least I hope I
hope, Gon-na push that day-dream, up the moun - tain

will, Gon - na build a moun-tain, gon-na build it
slope, Gon - na build a day-dream. gon-na see it

high, I don't know how I'm gon - na do it,
through, Gonna build a moun-tain and a day - dream,

on - ly know I'm gon - na try.
gon - na make 'em both come true.

3. Gonna build a heaven from a little hell,
Gonna build a heaven, and I know darn well,
If I build my mountain with a lot of care,
And take my day-dream up the mountain,
Heaven will be waiting there.

4. When I've built that heaven, as I will some day,
And the Lord sends Gabriel to take me away,
Wanna fine young son to take my place,
I'll leave a son in my heaven on earth,
With the Lord's good grace.

5. Gonna build a heaven from a little hell,
Gonna build a heaven and I know well,
With a fine young son who will take my place,
There'll be a sun in my heaven on earth,
With the good Lord's grace.

6. (As 1.)

14
Once In A Lifetime

Words & Music by Leslie Bricusse & Anthony Newley

15
Boy For Sale

Words & Music by Lionel Bart

One boy! Boy for sale!____ He's go-ing cheap! On-ly sev-en
('Ow much then?)

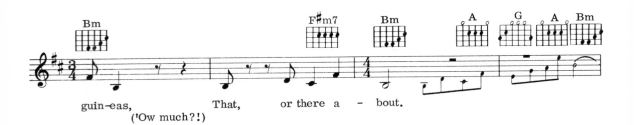

guin-eas, That, or there a - bout.
('Ow much?!)

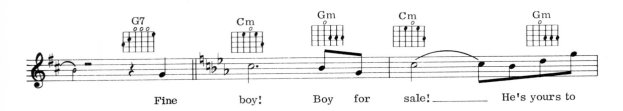

Fine boy! Boy for sale!_____ He's yours to

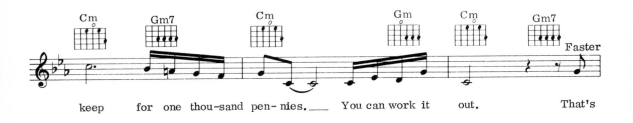

keep for one thou-sand pen-nies.__ You can work it out. That's

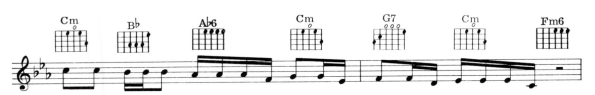

four pounds, 3 and 4; slight-ly un-der four guin-eas, knock'd down from se-ven guin-eas'.
(3 pounds 10
shillings)

Three pounds what sir! Certain-ly not, sir! An-y ad -vance on three pounds ten, then?

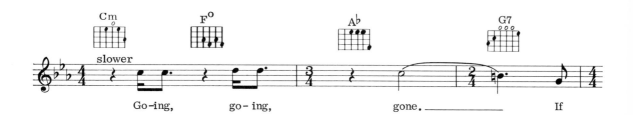

slower

Go-ing, go-ing, gone. _____ If

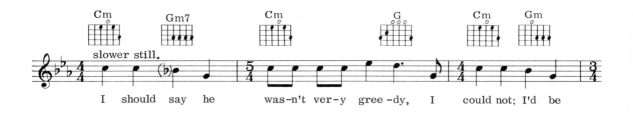

slower still.

I should say he was-n't ver-y gree-dy, I could not; I'd be

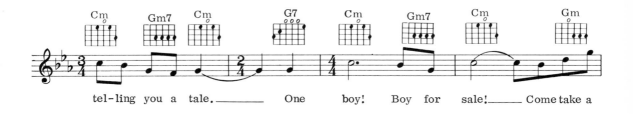

tel-ling you a tale. _____ One boy! Boy for sale! _____ Come take a

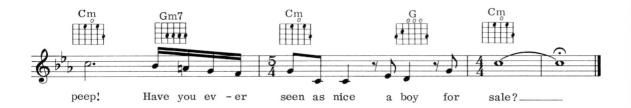

peep! Have you ev -er seen as nice a boy for sale? _____

16
All Good Gifts

Words & Music by Stephen Schwartz

We plough the fields_and scat-ter the good seed on_ the land, But
thank Thee then,_ oh Fa-ther, for all things bright and good, The

it is fed_ and wa-tered by God's al-might-y hand.___ He
seed time and_ the har-vest, our life, our health, our food.___ No

sends the snow_ in win-ter, the warmth to swell_ the grain, The
gifts have we_ to of-fer for all thy love_ im-parts, But

breez-es and_ the sun-shine and soft re-fresh-ing rain.___
that which Thou_ de-sir-est our hum-ble, thank-ful hearts.___

All good gifts a-round___ us___

are sent from heav-en a-bove.___

17
Being Alive

Words & Music by Stephen Sondheim

18
Company

Words & Music by Stephen Sondheim

19
Consider Yourself

Words & Music by Lionel Bart

20
I'd Do Anything

Words & Music by Lionel Bart

21
If You Could See Her

Words by Fred Ebb
Music by John Kander

22
Food Glorious Food

Words & Music by Lionel Bart

23
The Good Old Bad Old Days

Words and Music by Leslie Bricusse and Anthony Newley

24
If My Friends Could See Me Now

Words by Dorothy Fields
Music by Cy Coleman

25
Hey There

Words & Music by Richard Adler & Jerry Ross

Slow and expressively

Hey There, ___ you with the stars in your eyes,

Love ne - ver made a fool of you, You used to be too

wise! ___ Hey There, ___ you on that high ___ fly-ing

cloud, Though she won't throw a crumb to you, You

think some day she'll come to you. ___ Bet - ter for -

26
Baby Face

Words & Music by Harry Akst & Benny Davis

27
I Could Have Danced All Night

Words by Alan Jay Lerner
Music by Frederick Loewe

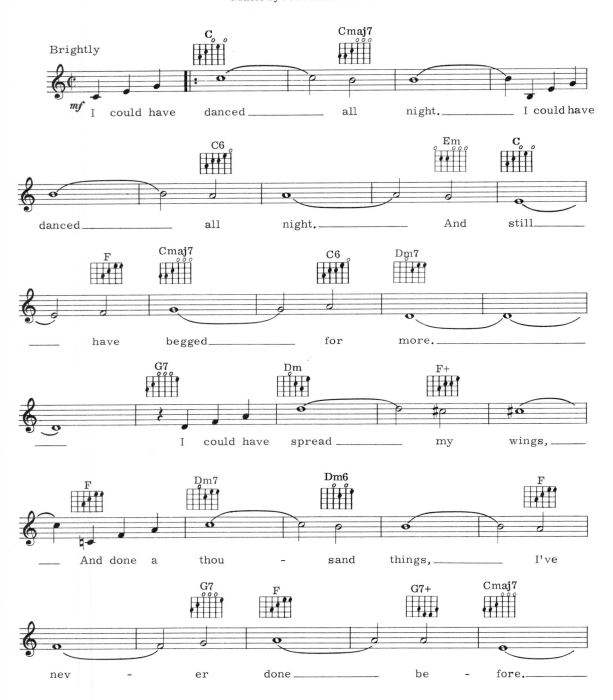

28
Feelin' Good

Words & Music by Leslie Bricusse and Anthony Newley

You know what I mean. Sleep in peace when day is done, That's what I mean.__ And this

old world is a new world and a bold world _____ for _____ me. _____

Stars when you shine, You know how I feel.

Scent on the pine, You know how I feel. Free-dom is mine, I know how I feel. It's a

new dawn, it's a new day, it's a new life _____ for _____ me. _____ Feel-ing

Good. _____

29
The Joker

Words & Music by Leslie Bricusse and Anthony Newley

There's al-ways a Jok-er in the pack, There's al-ways a lone-ly
(card-board)*

clown._____ The poor laugh-ing fool falls on his back, And
(paint-ed)*

ev-'ry one laughs when he's down. There's al-ways a fun-ny man__

_____ in the game, But he's on-ly fun-ny by mis-take. But

ev-'ry-one laughs at him _____ just the same, They don't see his lone-ly heart
(paint-ed)*

* words as in stage production

30
I Remember It Well

Words by Alan Jay Lerner
Music by Frederick Loewe

31
It's A Fine Life

Words & Music by Lionel Bart

Moderato

1. Small pleas-ures, small pleas-ures who would de-ny us these?
2. Who cares if strait la-ces sneer at us in the street.
3. No flounc-es, no feath-ers, No frills and fur-bi-loes.

Gin tod-dies, large mea-sures, No skimp-ing if you please!
Fine airs and fine gra-ces, Don't have to sin to eat.
All winds and all weath-ers, Ain't good for fan-cy clo'es.

I rough it, I love it, Life is a game of chance.
We wan-der through Lon-don, Who knows what we may find.
These trap-pings, these tat-ters, These we can just af-ford.

I'll ne-ver tire of it, Lead-ing this mer-ry dance. If you
There's pock-ets left un-done on man-y a be-hind. If you
What fu-ture? What mat-ters? We've got our bed and board. If you

don't mind having to go with-out things, It's a fine life! It's a fine life! Tho' it
don't mind taking it like it turns out, It's a fine life! It's a fine life! Keep the
don't mind having to deal with Fa-gin, It's a fine life! It's a fine life! Tho' dis-

ain't all jol-ly old pleasure out-ings, It's a fine life! It's a fine life! When you've
can-dle burning un-til it burns out, It's a fine life! It's a fine life! Tho' you
eased rats threaten to bring the plague in, It's a fine life! It's a fine life! But the

got some—one to love, You for — get your cares and strife. Let the
some—times do come by, The oc — ca — sion—al black eye. You can
grass is green and dense, On the right side of the fence. And we

prudes look down on us, Let the wide world frown on us. It's a fine, fine life.
al —ways cov—er one, While he blacks the oth—er one, But you don't dare cry.
take good care of it, That we get our share of it, And we don't mean

If you don't mind having to like or lump it, It's a

fine life! It's a fine life! Tho' there's no tea sip—ping and eat—ing crum—pet, It's a

fine life! It's a fine life! Not for me the hap—py home, hap—py

husband, hap—py wife. Tho' it sometimes touch—es me for the likes of such as me. Mine's a

fine, fine life.

32
Make Believe

Music by Jerome Kern
Words by Oscar Hammerstein II

We could make be-lieve — I love you, —

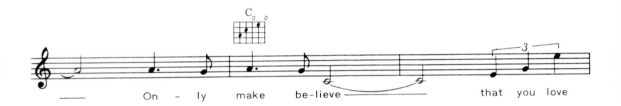

— On - ly make be-lieve — that you love

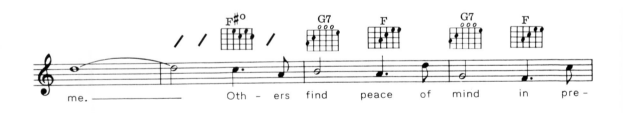

me. — Oth - ers find peace of mind in pre-

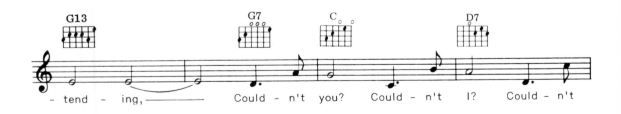

- tend - ing, — Could - n't you? Could - n't I? Could - n't

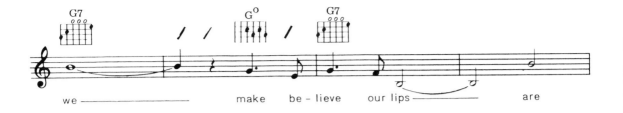

we ——————— make be - lieve our lips ———— are

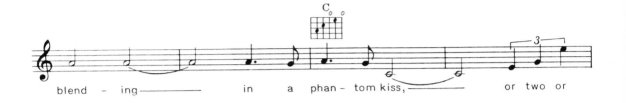

blend - ing ————— in a phan - tom kiss, ———— or two or

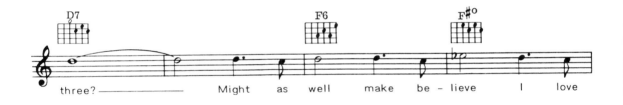

three? ————— Might as well make be - lieve I love

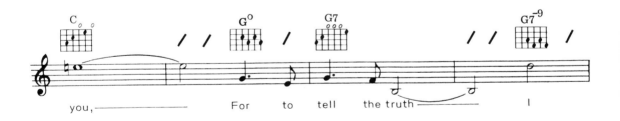

you, ————— For to tell the truth ———— I

do. ————— We could do. —————

33
Let The Sunshine In

Words by James Rado & Gerome Ragni
Music by Galt MacDermot

34
Little Tin Box

Words by Sheldon Harnick
Music by Jerry Bock

35
Married

Words by Fred Ebb
Music by John Kander

36
The Last Supper

Words by Tim Rice
Music by Andrew Lloyd Webber

37
Never Smile At A Crocodile

Words by Jack Lawrence
Music by Frank Churchill

38
Oliver

Words & Music by Lionel Bart

39
On The Street Where You Live

Words by Alan Jay Lerner
Music by Frederick Loewe

40
My Kind Of Girl

Words & Music by Leslie Bricusse

41
Mein Herr

Words by Fred Ebb
Music by John Kander

42
Oom Pah Pah

Words & Music by Lionel Bart

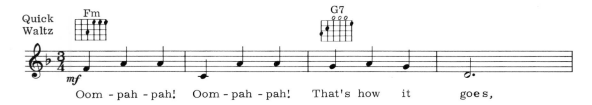

Oom - pah - pah! Oom - pah - pah! That's how it goes,

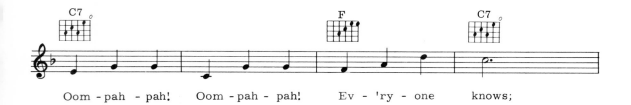

Oom - pah - pah! Oom - pah - pah! Ev - 'ry - one knows;

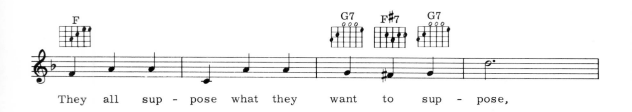

They all sup - pose what they want to sup - pose,

When they hear Oom - pah - pah! _____

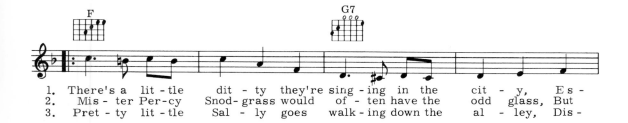

1. There's a lit - tle dit - ty they're sing - ing in the cit - y, Es -
2. Mis - ter Per - cy Snod - grass would of - ten have the odd glass, But
3. Pret - ty lit - tle Sal - ly goes walk - ing down the al - ley, Dis -

43
On This Night Of
A Thousand Stars

Words by Tim Rice
Music by Andrew Lloyd Webber

1. On this night of a thou-sand stars,_
(2) twink-ling lights,_

let me take you to hea-ven's door,_ Where the mu-sic of
we shall love through e-ter-ni-ty,_ On this night in a

love's gui-tars____ plays for ev-er-more.
mil-lion nights___ fly a-way with me.

In the glow of those I nev-er dreamed that a kiss could be as

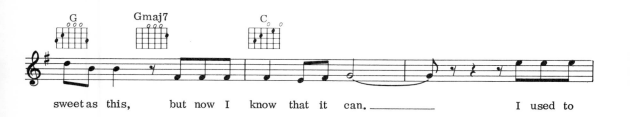

sweet as this, but now I know that it can._____ I used to

44
It's So Easy

Words & Music by Buddy Holly & Norman Petty

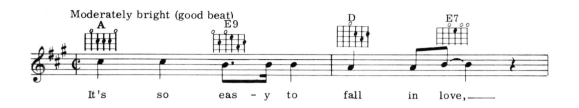

It's   so   eas-y to   fall   in   love,____

It's   so   eas-y to ____ fall ____ in   love. ____

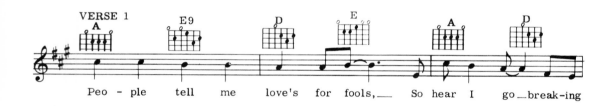

VERSE 1

Peo-ple   tell   me   love's   for   fools, ____ So hear I   go __ break-ing

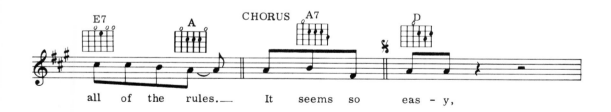

all   of   the   rules. ____   It   seems   so   eas-y,

so   dog-gone   eas-y;

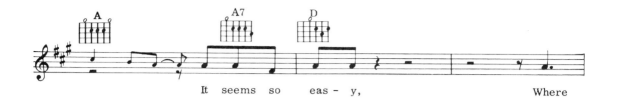

It seems so eas - y, Where

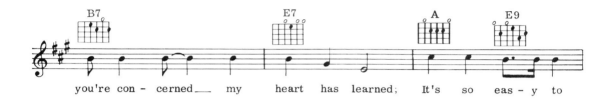

you're con - cerned my heart has learned; It's so eas - y to

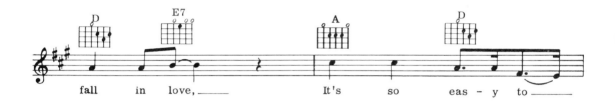

fall in love, It's so eas - y to

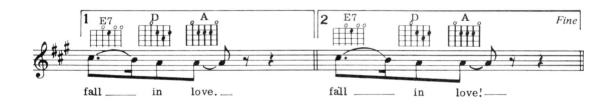

1 fall in love. **2** fall in love! *Fine*

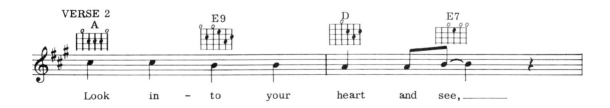

VERSE 2

Look in - to your heart and see,

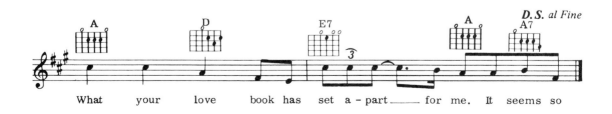

D.S. al Fine

What your love book has set a - part for me. It seems so

45
Pick A Pocket Or Two

Words & Music by Lionel Bart

46
Stranger In Paradise

Words & Music by Robert Wright & George Forrest

47
Reviewing The Situation

Words & Music by Lionel Bart

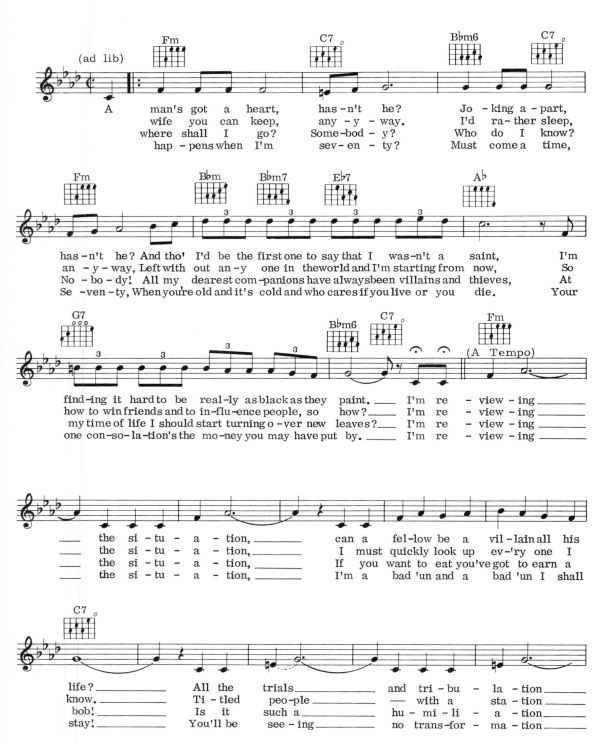

48
Peggy Sue

Words & Music by Jerry Allison, Norman Petty & Buddy Holly

Peg - gy Sue; _____ Oh, well, I

love you gal, __ and I need you, Peg - gy Sue. _____

I love you, _____

Peg - gy Sue, _____ With a love so rare and true, _

_____ Oh, Peg - gy, _____ My Peg - gy Sue; _

_____ Oh, well, I love you, gal, _

_ Yes, I want you, Peg - gy Sue. _____

D.S. al Fine

Fine

49
Someone Is Waiting

Words & Music by Stephen Sondheim

50
Poor Wandering One

Words by W. S. Gilbert
Music by Arthur Sullivan

51
Talk To The Animals
Words & Music by Leslie Bricusse

52
Thank Heaven For Little Girls

Words by Alan Jay Lerner
Music by Frederick Loewe

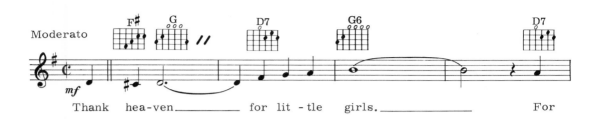

Thank hea-ven____ for lit-tle girls.____ For

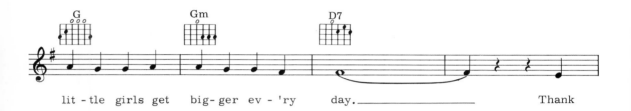

lit-tle girls get big-ger ev-'ry day.____ Thank

hea-ven____ for lit-tle girls.____ They

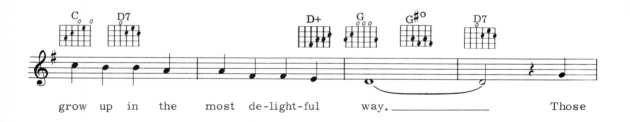

grow up in the most de-light-ful way.____ Those

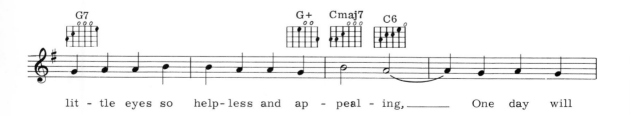

lit-tle eyes so help-less and ap-peal-ing,____ One day will

53
Thoroughly Modern Millie

Words by Sammy Cahn
Music by James Van Heusen

54
'Til Tomorrow

Words by Sheldon Harnick
Music by Jerry Bock

55
Matchmaker

Words by Sheldon Harnick
Music by Jerry Bock

56
When A Felon's Not Engaged In His Employment

Words by W. S. Gilbert
Music by Arthur Sullivan

1. When a fel-on's not en-gaged in his em-ploy-ment (his em-ployment) or ma-
2. When the en-ter-pris-ing bur-glar's not a-bur-gling (not a-bur-gling) When the

tur-ing his fe-lo-nious lit-tle plans, His ca-
cut throat is-n't oc-cu-pied in crime, He

pac-i-ty for in-no-cent en-joy-ment (-cent en-joy-ment) Is
loves to hear the lit-tle brook a-gur-gling (brook a-gur-gling) And

just as great as a-ny hon-est man's. Our
lis-ten to the mer-ry vil-lage chime. When the

feel-ings we with dif-fi-cul-ty smoth-er, When con-
cos-ter's fin-ished jump-ing on his moth-er, He

stab - u - la - ry du - ty's to be done.⌉ Ah, take
loves to lie a - bask - ing in the sun.⌋

one con - sid - er - a - tion with an - oth - er, A po -

lice - man's lot is not a hap - py one. When con -

stab - u - la - ry du - ty's to be done, to be done, A po -

1.
lice - man's lot is not a hap - py one, hap - py one. *mp*

2.
one, hap - py one. (instrumental)

57
Where Is Love

Words & Music by Lionel Bart

58
When Frederic Was
A Little Lad

Words by W. S. Gilbert
Music by Arthur Sullivan

59
Who Will Buy

Words & Music by Lionel Bart

Who Will Buy this won-der-ful morn - ing?

Such a sky you nev - er did see. ___

Who will tie it up with a rib - bon, And

put it in a box for me? ___ So I can / There'll nev - er

see it at my lei - sure ___ When ev - er / be a day so sun - ny, ___ It could not

things go wrong, ___ And I would keep it / hap - pen twice. ___ Where is the man with

60
What Ought We To Do

Words by W. S. Gilbert
Music by Arthur Sullivan

61
Willkommen

Words by Fred Ebb
Music by John Kander

62
A Dream Is A Wish
Your Heart Makes

Words & Music by Mack David, Al Hoffman & Jerry Livingston

63
Hair

Words by James Rado & Gerome Ragni
Music by Galt MacDermot

64
Jailhouse Rock

Words & Music by Jerry Leiber & Mike Stoller

The war-den threw a par-ty in the Coun-ty jail, The
Spi-der Mur-phy play'd the ten-or sax-o-phone,

pri-son band was there and they be-gan to wail, The
Lit-tle Joe was blow-in' on the slide trom-bone, The

band was jump-in' and the joint be-gan to swing. You
drum-mer boy from Il-li-nois went crash, boom, bang' The

CHORUS

should-'ve heard those knocked —out — jail-birds sing.
whole — rhy-thm sec-tion was the Pur-ple Gang. Let's Rock'

Let's Rock!   Ev-'ry-bo-dy in the whole cell block

Was a-dan-cin' to the jail-house Rock!

65
Tomorrow Belongs To Me

Words by Fred Ebb
Music by John Kander

66
Typically English

Words & Music by Leslie Bricusse & Anthony Newley

67
Ain't Misbehavin'

Words by Andy Razaf
Music by Thomas Waller & Harry Brooks

68
How About You

Words by Ralph Freed
Music by Burton Lane

69
Aquarius

Words by James Rado & Gerome Ragni
Music by Galt MacDermot

70
Cabaret

Words by Fred Ebb
Music by John Kander

71
I'll Never Fall In Love Again

Words by Hal David
Music by Burt Bacharach

72
Maybe This Time

Words by Fred Ebb
Music by John Kander

73
Money, Money

Words by Fred Ebb
Music by John Kander

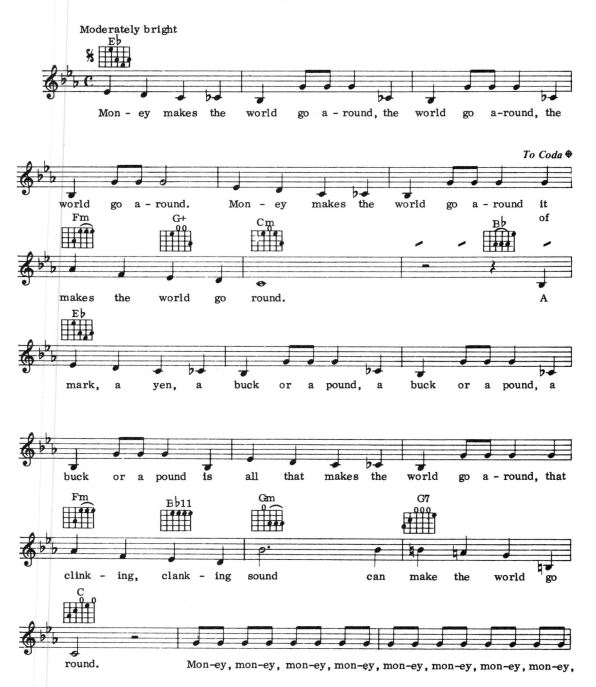

mon-ey, mon-ey, mon-ey, mon-ey. If you hap-pen to be rich, and you feel like a

night's en-ter-tain-ment, you can pay for a gay es-ca-pade. If you hap-pen to be

rich, and a-lone, and you need a com-pan-ion, you can ring ting-a-ling for the

tacet - - - - -*

maid. If you hap-pen to be rich and you find you are left by your lov-er, tho' you

moan and you groan quite a lot, you can take it on the chin, call a cab. and be-

D.%. al Coda

-gin to re-cov-er on your four-teen ca-rat yacht. What?

CODA

that we both are sure, On be-ing poor.

74
Take That Look Off Your Face

Words by Don Black
Music by Andrew Lloyd Webber

75
All Shook Up

Words & Music by Otis Blackwell and Elvis Presley

A-well-a, Bless my soul, what's wrong with me? I'm itch-ing like a man on a fuz-zy tree. My friends say I'm act-ing queer as a bug, I'm in love, I'm all shook up! Mm mm oh, oh, yeah, yeah, My hands are sha-ky and my knees are weak, I can't seem to stand on my own two feet. Who do you thank when you have such luck? I'm in love! I'm all shook up! Mm mm, mm, oh, oh, yeah, yeah!

76
If I Were A Rich Man

Words by Sheldon Harnick
Music by Jerry Bock

77
Easy To Be Hard

Words by James Rado & Gerome Ragni
Music by Galt MacDermot

78
You Can Fly You Can Fly
You Can Fly

Words by Sammy Cahn
Music by Sammy Fain

79
Tell Me On A Sunday
Words by Don Black
Music by Andrew Lloyd Webber

80
Promises Promises

Words by Hal David
Music by Burt Bacharach

81
Superstar

Words by Tim Rice
Music by Andrew Lloyd Webber

Ev -'ry time I look at you I don't un -der - stand, _____

Why you let the things you did get so out of hand. _____

You'd have man - aged bet - ter if you'd had _____ it planned, _____

Why'd you choose such a back-ward time and such a strange land? _____

If you'd come to - day you would have reached a whole na - tion,

Is - rael in Four B. C. had no mass com - mu - ni - ca - tion.

Don't you get me wrong, ___ Don't you get me wrong, ___ Don't you get me wrong, ___

82
Sunrise Sunset

Words by Sheldon Harnick
Music by Jerry Bock

83
Eternally

Words by Geoffrey Parsons & John Turner
Music by Charles Chaplin

84
Raindrops Keep Falling On My Head

Words by Hal David
Music by Burt Bacharach

85
Don't Cry For Me Argentina

Words by Tim Rice
Music by Andrew Lloyd Webber

86
Bye Bye Baby

Words by Leo Robin
Music by Jule Styne

87
This Is My Song

Words & Music by Charles Chaplin

Barcarolle

Why is my heart so light? Why are the stars so bright? Why is the sky so blue _____ since the hour _____ I met you? _____ A - lone I sing in moon - light _____ with you in my heart su - preme, _____ To hear you say "I love _____ you", That is my hope, my

88
Can't Help Lovin' Dat Man

Music by Jerome Kern
Words by Oscar Hammerstein II

89
They Didn't Believe Me

Music by Jerome Kern
Words by Herbert Reynolds

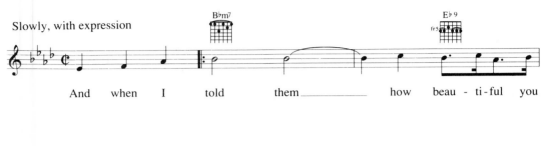

And when I told them ___ how beau-ti-ful you

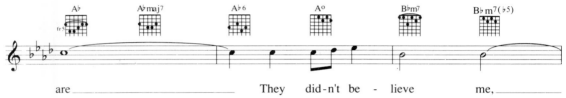

are ___ They did-n't be - lieve me, ___

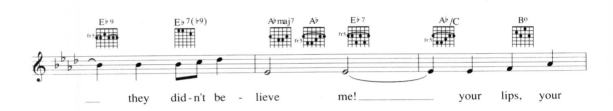

___ they did-n't be - lieve me! ___ your lips, your

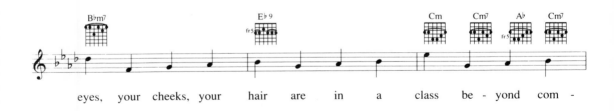

eyes, your cheeks, your hair are in a class be - yond com -

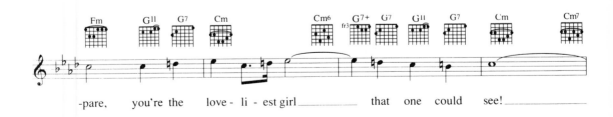

-pare, you're the love - li - est girl ___ that one could see! ___

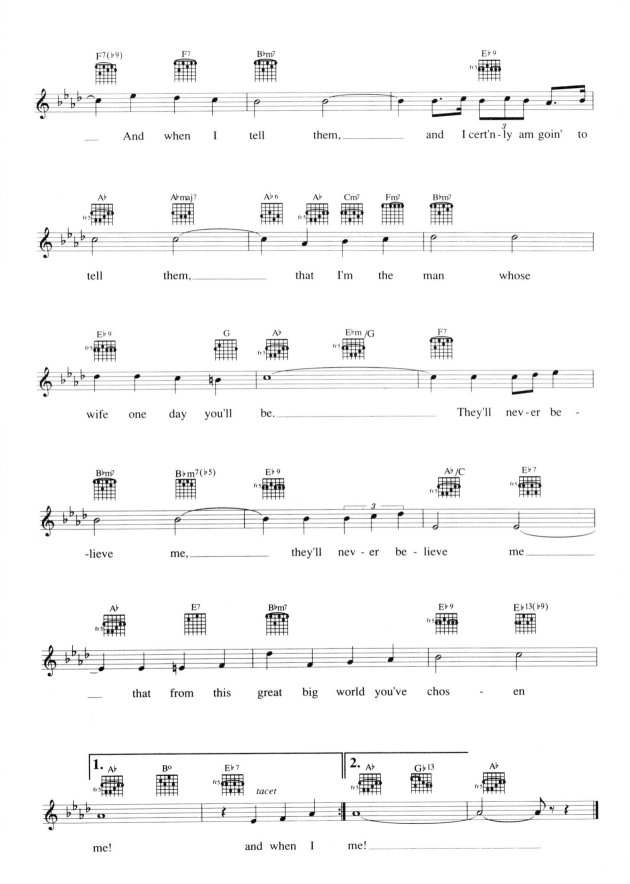

90
That'll Be The Day

Words & Music by Norman Petty, Buddy Holly & Jerry Allison

Medium Rock

Well, you give me all your lov-in' and your tur - tle dov-in', All_

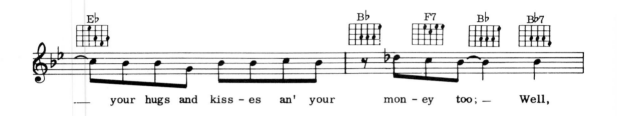

___ your hugs and kiss - es an' your mon - ey too; — Well,

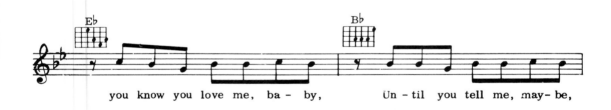

you know you love me, ba - by, Un - til you tell me, may-be,

that some - day, well, I'll be through! Well,— That'll be the day, when

you say, good - bye, Yes, ____ That - 'll be the day, when

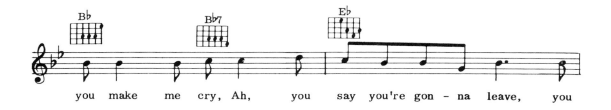

you make me cry, Ah, you say you're gon - na leave, you

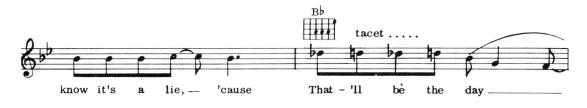

know it's a lie, — 'cause That - 'll be the day _____

— when I die. — Well, — when I die. —

VERSE 2

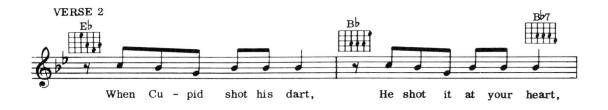

When Cu - pid shot his dart, He shot it at your heart,

So if we ev - er part and I leave you, You say you told me an' you

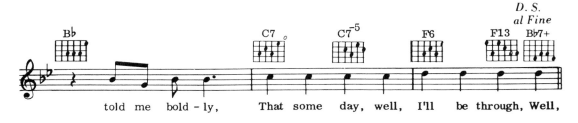

told me bold - ly, That some day, well, I'll be through, Well,

91
True Love Ways

Words & Music by Buddy Holly & Norman Petty

92
Maybe Baby

Words & Music by Charles Hardin & Norman Petty

93
Rave On

Words & Music by Sunny West, Bill Tilghman & Norman Petty

Bright beat

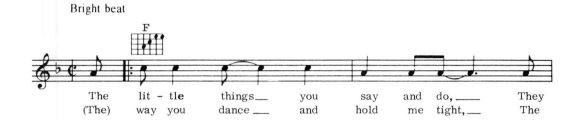

The lit - tle things__ you say and do, __ They
(The) way you dance __ and hold me tight, __ The

make me want to be with you ____ hoo - hoo,
way you kiss and say good - ni - hi - hight,

Rave on! It's a cra - zy feel - in' and I know it 's ____

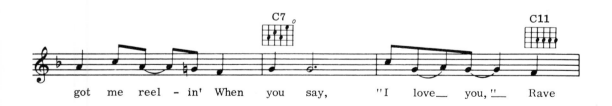

got me reel - in' When you say, "I love__ you, "__ Rave

On. _____ Well, ____ the   On. _____

CHORUS

Well -ell -ell, Rave On! It's a cra - zy feel - in' and

I know it's ___ got me reel - in', I'm so glad that

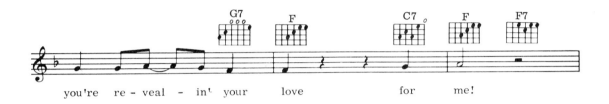

you're re - veal - in' your love for me!

Rave On, Rave On and tell ___ me, Tell me not ___

___ to be lone - ly, Tell me you love me on - ly,

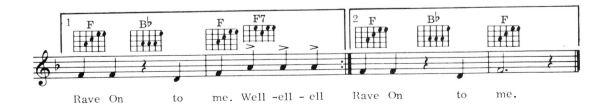

Rave On to me. Well -ell -ell Rave On to me.

94
Ready Teddy

Words & Music by John Marascalco & Robert Blackwell

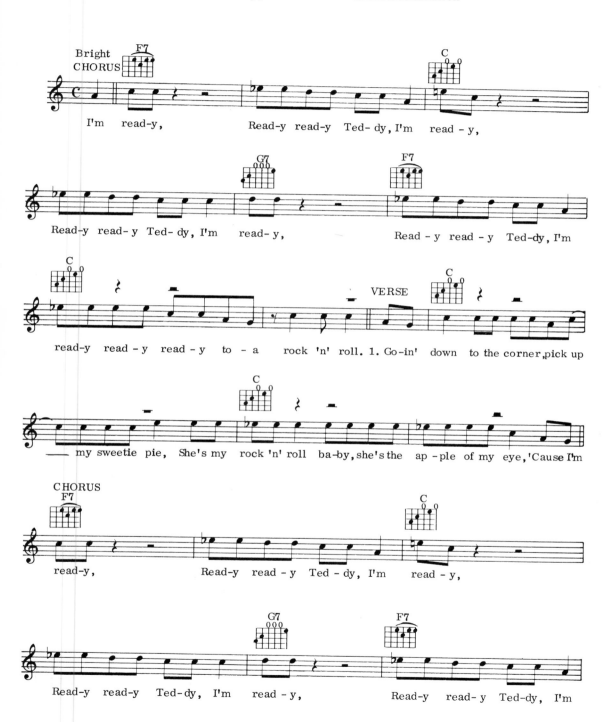

read-y read-y read-y to-a rock 'n' roll. 2. Well, the flat top cats and the
kick off my shoes, roll —

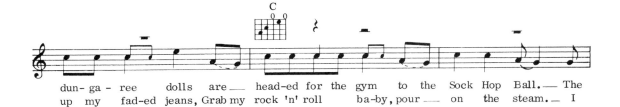

dun-ga-ree dolls are — head-ed for the gym to the Sock Hop Ball. — The
up my fad-ed jeans, Grab my rock 'n' roll ba-by, pour — on the steam. — I

joint is real-ly jump-in', the cats are go-in' wild. — The mu-sic real-ly sends me. I
shuf-fle to the left, I shuf-fle to the right. Gon-na rock 'n' roll till the

CHORUS

dig that cra-zy style, 'Cause I'm ⎰ Read-y, read-y read-y Ted-dy, I'm
ear-ly ear-ly night, 'Cause I'm ⎱

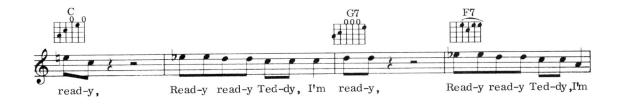

read-y, Read-y read-y Ted-dy, I'm read-y, Read-y read-y Ted-dy, I'm

read-y read-y read-y to-a rock 'n' roll. 3. Gon-na rock 'n' roll.

95
Raining In My Heart

Words & Music by Boudleaux & Felice Bryant

Slowly

The sun is out, the sky is blue, there's

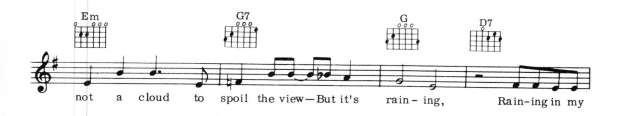

not a cloud to spoil the view—But it's rain - ing,   Rain-ing in my

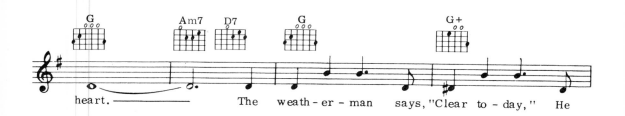

heart. ———   The weath - er - man   says, "Clear to-day,"   He

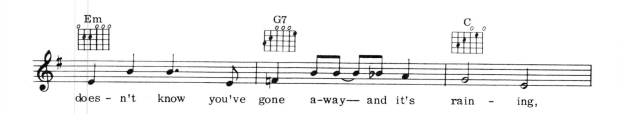

does - n't know   you've gone a-way— and it's   rain - ing,

Rain-ing in my heart. —— Oh, mis-er - y, mis - er -

y, ————————— What's gon- na be-come ———— of

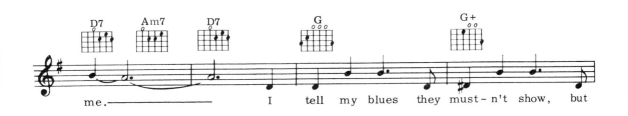

me. ——————— I tell my blues they must- n't show, but

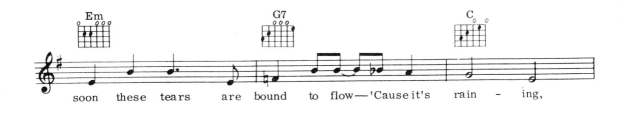

soon these tears are bound to flow —'Cause it's rain - ing,

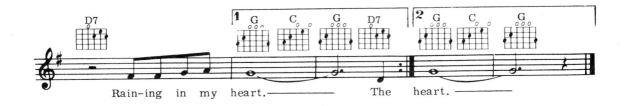

Rain-ing in my heart. ———— The heart. ————

96
Sweet Charity

Words by Dorothy Fields
Music by Cy Coleman

97
Day By Day

Words & Music by Stephen Schwartz

98
Chantilly Lace
Words & Music by J.P. Richardson

CHORUS

Moderate boogie woogie

Chan - til -ly Lace_____ and a pret-ty face_____ and a pon-y tail

_____ hang-in' down, _____ A wig-gle in her walk and a gig-gle in her

talk, They're gon - na make the world go 'round. _____ Ain't

noth-ing in the world like a big eyed girl _____ to make me act so fun-ny, spend my

dog - gone mon-ey, I feel real loose like a long necked goose, like a

Wa, ba-by that's what I like!___ (Spoken) (1) Huh?
(2) Huh? ha ha ha

Will I what? Do I what?
Huh? What's that? Pick you up at eight? And don't be late?

Will I what? Can't never tell baby?
You gotta be jokin' woman, I thought you might

ha ha ha ha I might,
pick me up at eight and don't be late.

but honey you know what I like.
It don't make no difference baby, you know what I really like.

Chan-til-ly Lace___ Chan-til-ly Lace what I like!___

Verse 3 (patter) Woo ha ha ha ha ha honey, you're tearin' me up on this telephone.
I swear I don't know what I'm gonna do with you, you yap and yap
and yap and yap and yap but when you break it all down you know
what I like.   (to Chorus)

99
I Don't Know How To Love Him

Words by Tim Rice
Music by Andrew Lloyd Webber

100
Over The Rainbow

Words by E. Y. Harburg
Music by Harold Arlen

101
Fiddler On The Roof

Words by Sheldon Harnick
Music by Jerry Bock

goes.
can.
What does it mean, this fid-dler on the roof, Who

fid-dles ev - 'ry night and fid-dles ev - 'ry noon? Why should he pick so

1
cu - ri - ous a place to play his lit-tle fid - dler's tune? 2. An

2
tune? A fid - dler on the roof, A

most un - like - ly sight, It might not mean a

thing, But then a - gain it might!